Developing Sci

DEVELOPING SCIENTIFIC SKILLS AND KNOWLEDGE

year

4

Christine Moorcroft

A & C BLACK

Contents

Friction

Circuits and conductors

Reprinted 2005
Published 2004 by A&C Black Publishers Limited
38 Soho Square, London W1D 3HB
www.acblack.com

ISBN-10: 0-7136-6643-9
ISBN-13: 978-0-7136-6643-4

Copyright text © Christine Moorcroft, 2004
Copyright illustrations © David Benham, 2004
Copyright cover illustration © Kay Widdowson, 2004
Editor: Jane Klima
Design: Bet Ayer

The author and publishers would like to thank Catherine Yemm, Trevor Davies and the staff of Balsall Common Primary School for their assistance in producing this series of books.

A CIP catalogue record for this book is available from the British Library.

Printed in Great Britain by St Edmundsbury Press Ltd, Bury St Edmunds, Suffolk.

A&C Black uses paper produced with elemental chlorine-free pulp, harvested from managed sustainable forests.

Introduction

Developing Science is a series of seven photocopiable activity books for science lessons. Each book provides a range of activities that not only develop children's knowledge and understanding of science, but also provide opportunities to develop their scientific skills: planning experimental work and obtaining and considering evidence.

The activities vary in their approach: some are based on first-hand observations, some present the findings of investigations for the children to analyse and others require the children to find information from books and electronic sources. They focus on different parts of a scientific investigation: questioning, responding to questions, generating ideas, planning, predicting, carrying out a fair test or an investigation, recording findings, checking and questioning findings, explaining findings and presenting explanations.

The activities in **Year 4** are based on Science in the National Curriculum and the QCA scheme of work for Year 4. They provide opportunities for the children to:

- develop curiosity about the things they observe and experience, and explore the world about them with all their senses;
- use this experience to develop their understanding of key scientific ideas and make links between different phenomena and experiences;
- begin to think about models to represent things they cannot directly experience;
- try to make sense of phenomena, seeking explanations and thinking critically about claims and ideas;
- acquire and refine the practical skills needed to investigate questions safely;
- develop skills of predicting, asking questions, making inferences, concluding and evaluating (based on evidence and understanding), and to use these skills in investigative work;
- practise mathematical skills such as counting, ordering numbers, measuring using standard and non-standard measures, and recording and interpreting simple charts;
- learn why numerical and mathematical skills are useful and helpful to understanding;
- think creatively about science and enjoy trying to make sense of phenomena;
- develop language skills through talking about their work and presenting their own ideas, using systematic writing of different kinds;
- use scientific and mathematical language (including technical vocabulary and conventions) and draw pictures, diagrams and charts to communicate scientific ideas;
- read non-fiction and extract information from sources such as reference books or CD-ROMs;
- work with others, listening to their ideas and treating these with respect;
- develop respect for evidence and evaluate critically ideas which may or may not fit the evidence available;
- develop a respect for the environment and living things and for their own health and safety.

The activities are carefully linked with the National Literacy Strategy to give the children opportunities to develop their reading skills in finding information (for example, scanning a text, reading instructions and making notes) and to use a range of writing skills in presenting their findings (for example, labelling diagrams and writing reports). Science-related vocabulary to introduce is provided in the **Notes on the activities** on pages 5–13.

Teachers are encouraged to introduce the activities presented in this book in a stimulating classroom environment. For example, you could provide investigation tables where the children can explore materials, equipment, pictures and books connected with the topics to be covered (such as habitats, solids and liquids, and electrical circuits).

Each activity sheet specifies the learning outcome and has a **Teachers' note** at the foot of the page, which you may wish to mask before photocopying. Expanded teaching notes are provided in the **Notes on the activities**. Most activities also end with a challenge (**Now try this!**), which reinforces the children's learning and provides the teacher with an opportunity for assessment. These extension activities might be appropriate for only a few children; it is not expected that the whole class should complete them. They should be completed in a notebook or on a separate sheet of paper.

Health and safety

Developing Science recognises the importance of safety in science lessons and provides advice on the ways in which teachers can make their lessons as safe as possible (including links to useful websites). The books also suggest ways in which to encourage children to take appropriate responsibility for their own safety. Teachers are recommended to follow the safety guidelines provided in the QCA scheme of work or in *Be Safe!* (available from the Association for Science Education). Specific health and safety advice is included in the **Notes on the activities** and warnings to the children feature on the activity sheets where relevant.

Online resources

In addition to the photocopiable activity sheets in this book, a collection of online science resources is available on the A & C Black website at www.acblack.com/developingscience. These activities can be used either as stand-alone teaching resources or in conjunction with the printed sheets. An **ICT** icon on an activity page indicates that there is a resource on the website specifically designed to complement that activity.

To enable them to be used by children of a wide range of abilities, all of the activities on the website feature both written and spoken instructions. The tasks have been designed to provide experiences which are not easy to reproduce in the classroom.

These notes expand upon those provided at the foot of the activity pages. They give ideas for making the most of the activity sheet, including suggestions for the whole-class introduction, the plenary session or for follow-up work using an adapted version of the activity sheet. To help teachers to select appropriate learning experiences for their pupils, the activities are grouped into sections within each book, but the pages need not be presented in the order in which they appear, unless stated otherwise. Where appropriate, links to other areas of the curriculum are indicated, in particular literacy and numeracy.

Moving and growing

ICT **Dry bones** (page 14) could be introduced by singing the African spiritual *Dem Bones*, with the children performing the actions. (See http://ingeb.org/spiritua/demdrybo.html for the words.) Ask the children to feel some of the bones in their bodies and to say which ones are joined and where. Ask them to name any bones and joints they know. Ask them why they have three bones in their arms, several bones in their hands and so on. If possible, provide a model skeleton for them to examine (you might be able to borrow one from a secondary school, college or teachers' centre). Some children might be able to learn the medical names for the bones. A complementary activity for this sheet is available on the website (see Year 4 Activity 1).

> **Vocabulary:** *ankle, backbone, elbow, joint, knee, knuckle, rib, shoulder, skeleton, spine, wrist.*

ICT For **Whose skeleton?** (page 15), if possible visit a museum (or a museum website) showing the skeletons of various animals. Before the visit, discuss what the children can find out Visits must be planned in accordance with school and LEA guidelines.
about animals from their skeletons: for example, which of their bones are similar to those of humans, which bones they have that humans do not have, and why. The children could prepare simple questions of their own: for example: 'Do fish/snakes have ribs?' 'Do monkeys/dogs/elephants/cattle have bones in their tails?' On outline shapes of animals they could draw the animals' skeletons, using real skeletons or pictures to help them. This page could be linked with literacy (revising punctuation of sentences). A complementary activity for this sheet is available on the website (see Year 4 Activity 2).

> **Resources:** pictures of various animals and models or pictures of animals' skeletons

> **Vocabulary:** *compare, difference, ribs, similarity, skeleton, tail.*

Our growing bones (page 16) encourages the children to think about the types of questions that can be answered by an investigation and how to plan an investigation. The children should realise that measuring only one Year 1 child and two Year 4 children is not enough to give a valid answer to the question. How many children do they think should be measured, and why? Point out that the bigger the sample the more accurate the results, but also discuss what size of sample is feasible. Invite the children to demonstrate which part of each child's arm they would measure each time: for instance, from the elbow to the wrist bone. This also revises mathematical skills (measuring length) and handling data.

> **Vocabulary:** *forearm, improve, length, longer, measure.*

In **A bony question** (page 17) the children should find that there is little difference between the sizes of the skulls of children in the two year groups. Some of them could plan and carry out a similar investigation on children from Nursery, Reception or Year 1 and Year 6 or between children of different ages and adults. Others could compare the sizes of forearms or lower leg bones. To link with literacy, they could prepare a radio or television report about their findings.

> **Resources:** tape measures

> **Vocabulary:** *compare, distance, forearm, length, measure, skull.*

Look – no bones! (page 18) helps children to understand that the purpose of the skeleton is to support the body. It introduces the terms *vertebrate* and *invertebrate* for animals with and without a backbone. During a PE lesson, before beginning the activity, ask the children to stand on a mat and then pretend they have no skeleton. What happens to their body? How does a skeleton help? You could also mention that bones help to protect parts of the body such as the brain (the skull) and the heart and lungs (the ribs). They could draw and cut out pictures of animals they have observed and glue them into sets labelled *Vertebrates* and *Invertebrates*. During literacy they could investigate the derivation of the words *vertebrate* and *invertebrate* and the use of prefixes to form opposites.

> **Resources:** real animals such as fish in a tank, caged pets, small animals collected from gardens, a park or the school grounds • magnifying glasses • pictures of vertebrates (such as mammals, reptiles, fish, amphibians and birds) and invertebrates (such as snails, slugs, spiders, worms, crabs, jellyfish)

> **Vocabulary:** *backbone, inside, invertebrate, outside, skeleton, support, vertebrate.*

Phew! (page 19) develops the children's understanding that the muscles work hard when the body is exercising. It also develops skills in observation and comparison. You could help the children to make a display of sports people before, during and For this activity the children should carry out the normal kinds of exercise they do during PE lessons and not push themselves to extremes.
after strenuous exercise, including the ways in which they help their bodies to recover after exercise. These could be discussed and the children could find out more about them: for example, why many sports people drink water and sometimes glucose drinks immediately after exercise, why they put on extra

clothing, why long-distance runners wrap themselves in foil blankets. After completing the activity, the children can feel their pulse beat on the inside of the wrist or the back of the knee (whichever they find easier). They should place a finger lightly on the spot where they can feel their pulse and count the beats. Revise how to use a stopwatch and how to read a thermometer (a stick-on forehead thermometer is the only safe way to take body temperature at school). In literacy lessons, they could write poems based on their observations.

> **Vocabulary:** *breathing, exercise, heartbeat, muscles, perspiration, sweat.*

Habitats

Is it alive? (page 20) prepares the children for subsequent work on animals and plants. Scientists use various criteria for defining 'living': for example, having the potential to reproduce and having the need for nutrients. Living things grow,

 The children should avoid touching their faces when handling animals or plants and should wash their hands afterwards.

respire, respond to their surroundings and excrete. Animals can also move from one place to another, whereas plant movement is on the spot. Terrestrial plants are considered to be stationary; the 'movement' of plants is over time, using runners, rhizomes and so on; other plant movement includes plants growing towards a light source; and some plants 'move' in response to other stimuli: for example, the Venus fly-trap closes its trap if anything touches the hairs in it, and many plants (such as daisies) open up in sunshine and close in darkness. Plants do not move independently from place to place as animals do. Encourage the children to explain how they decide whether something is living or not. Some of them might have difficulty with the tree in winter and the wooden table.

Answers:

Alive: bird, cat, flowers, fruit (it can reproduce because it contains seeds, which will grow into plants and then respire and feed – cooked or de-seeded fruit cannot be deemed to be living), grass, plant, tree (it will grow leaves in the spring). The outer epidermal layers of a plant may have a skin-like appearance, and could also have hairs. The fruit in the bowl should raise class discussion. (The cells of the fruit and the cut flowers continue to respire for several months before dying and then their seeds continue to respire and can reproduce.) Point out that seeds do not begin to sprout as soon as they land in the soil. They stay dormant (as if asleep) for several months; in fact some seeds, such as rowan, require a period of cold before they can germinate.

Not alive: bird table, curtains and other fabrics, furniture such as the chair, cupboard, table and television set, fire, logs, painting, sun. (Wooden items such as the bird table, logs and furniture were once alive but can no longer respond, grow or reproduce and no longer respire or feed.) If the children find this hard, encourage them to look for similarities between themselves and other living things.

> **Resources:** examples (and pictures) of animals and plants either in the classroom or outside (include trees, grass, insects, spiders, slugs or snails, worms, reptiles and mammals)

> **Vocabulary:** *alive, animal, breathe, excrete, grass, living, organism, plant, reproduce.*

Plant or animal? (page 21) develops the children's understanding of what is a plant and what is an animal. Most living things can be classified as plants or animals, but fungi are now considered to belong to a

 The children should avoid touching their faces when handling animals or plants and should wash their hands afterwards.

separate category – neither the plant nor the animal kingdom. When helping the children to decide which living things are animals and which are plants it is useful to consider what the organism can do. Some children include 'warm' and 'furry' in their definition of 'animal', and so might not include worms or snails. Ask them to think about how they know that a person is living. Can the animal do any of the same things? Does it need any of the same things? Worms and snails both need to respire (breathe); they can move and reproduce; they need food and they respond to things around them.

> **Resources:** examples (and pictures) of animals and plants either in the classroom or outside (include trees, grass, insects, spiders, slugs or snails, worms, reptiles and mammals)

> **Vocabulary:** *alive, animal, bat, breathe, grass, living, lizard, organism, plant, reproduce, robin, spider, sycamore.*

A place to live (page 22) develops the children's understanding of why certain animals are found in a particular habitat. They are encouraged to make predictions about the organisms to be found in a habitat. Before the children begin the activity sheet they should have the opportunity to observe conditions in a local habitat and to predict what living things they will find there; afterwards let them check their predictions and notice that animals are suited to the habitats in which they are found. Introduce the term *organism* for 'living thing'. Children who undertake the extension activity will also need to know the meaning of *conditions*. You could use a literacy lesson to write a non-chronological report about habitats.

> **Vocabulary:** *conditions, habitat, organism.*

Groups (page 23) shows children the different ways in which organisms can be grouped according to observable features. After completing the activity they could draw other organisms to add to each set and explain why they belong there. When the sets are large enough the children might be able to find ways of sub-dividing them.

 The children should avoid touching their faces when handling animals or plants and should wash their hands afterwards. Help the children to return animals to the place where they were found or to a similar place.

> **Resources:** plants and animals collected from a local habitat such as the school grounds or private land whose owners have given permission (it is illegal to pick flowers or dig up plants from roadsides and fields)

> **Vocabulary:** *animal, classify, features, group, habitat, organism, plant.*

Keys: 1 and **2** (pages 24–25) help the children to understand how a key is constructed and how to use it for identifying animals and plants. Some children might need practice in asking questions whose answer is *yes* or *no*. Suitable questions for **Keys: 1** include 'Does it have legs?', 'Does it have wings?', 'Does it have a sting?', 'Does it have six legs?', 'Does it have eight legs?' and 'Does it have a shell?' Before the children tackle **Keys: 2**, show them a selection of leaves, fruits and seeds from both coniferous and deciduous trees and ensure they understand the difference between needles and leaves. *Answers:* A Cypress; B London plane; C Norway spruce; D Rowan; E Sycamore; F Yew. Some children might be able to construct their own keys. Point out that the questions are useful only if they help to split a group into two. You could use the software program Flexitree for more guidance. To link this with literacy, ask the children to compile alphabetical glossaries or 'mini-encyclopedias' about living things.

> **Vocabulary:** *animal, cypress, group, London plane, Norway spruce, plant, question, rowan, sycamore, yew.*

 Asking questions and **Let's investigate** (pages 26–27) encourage the children to pose questions about organisms they can investigate. Ask them to read out their questions. Write up their questions in three sets (without headings): *Can be investigated* and (if necessary) *Cannot be investigated but can be looked up*, and *Cannot be answered.*

> During the planning of their investigations point out the sections of the planning sheet on page 27 that refer to health and safety and caring for the animals. Encourage the children to write their own rules.

After collecting the children's questions, ask them if they can tell how they are grouped. Point out the questions that can be investigated and ask the children if answers can be found to the other questions and, if so, how. What do they expect to find out? After the children have planned their investigations, discuss their ideas and provide an opportunity for them to carry them out and record their results. Did the results answer their question? How well? Is there anything else they need to do in order to find the answer? Discuss any surprises they had. A complementary activity for these sheets is available on the website (see Year 4 Activity 3).

> **Vocabulary:** *answer, earthworm, gerbil, goldfish, health, investigate, question, safety, snail, starling, woodlouse.*

What does it eat? (page 28) encourages children to make reliable observations of organisms, indicating whether their prediction was valid and explaining their findings in scientific terms. Discuss how the children will know which foods the animal ate the most of (they need to measure how much was provided and measure how much was eaten).

> During the planning of their investigations point out the sections of the planning sheet that refer to health and safety and caring for the animals under investigation. Encourage the children to write their own rules.

The quantities of food could be measured by spreading them out on squared paper and drawing around them before and after the investigation. The children could count the squares covered, record their measurements and deduce which foods the animal preferred (because it ate more of it than of other foods). This provides opportunities for developing mathematical skills. After the children have planned their investigations, discuss their ideas and provide an opportunity for them to carry them out and record their

results. Was the test fair? (Did the animal have the same opportunity to eat each food?)

> **Vocabulary:** *amount, fair, health, measure, observe, quantity, record, safety.*

Look it up (page 29) develops the children's knowledge of the food sources of different animals. Revise note-taking: remind the children to find short ways to write and to omit unimportant words like *a* and *the*. To enable them to find out about animals they cannot observe, provide information books, a television set and suitable videos, a computer, CD-ROMs and DVDs and access to the Internet. Useful resources include *Eyewitness Pond and River* (Dorling Kindersley). Ask the children to note only information that will help them to answer their question, and to record the source of the information.

> **Vocabulary:** *feeding habits, food, food source.*

Changing places (page 30) helps the children to recognise ways in which living things and the environment need protection. You could collect news items related to changes in habitats: for example, oil spills at sea, tree felling, building on open land, clearing undergrowth. The children could ask their own questions about habitats they know, and find out the answers with reference to the food chains of those habitats. As well as finding out how changes to the environment affect animals they could find out how this, in turn, affects the environment: for example, natural predators like ladybirds might be killed by insecticides sprayed onto plants to kill aphids; this, in turn, could lead to an increased need for pesticides to control aphids. In a literacy lesson, the children could write a newspaper report about a habitat they know which is being changed by people: for example, a pond filling with litter.

> **Vocabulary:** *affect, change, depend, environment, food chain, habitat, survive.*

Keeping warm

Feel the heat (page 31) demonstrates that the sense of touch is not an accurate way of judging temperature. After the children have completed the activity, introduce the word

> Ensure that 'very warm' water is not uncomfortably hot to the touch.

temperature and ask them if they know what it means. Where have they heard it used before? They might have heard it mentioned when they have their temperature taken when ill. Explain that every material has a temperature that can be measured, just as things have a height, weight and length that can be measured. Temperature is a measurement of how hot things are. Draw out the idea that testing temperature by touch is not an accurate way of measuring it and tell the children that in the next lesson they will learn a more accurate way of measuring temperature.

> **Resources:** two bowls, large enough for the children to put their hands in • a bucket • cold water • very warm water • lukewarm water

> **Vocabulary:** *accurate, cold, hot, icy, lukewarm, warm.*

Temperature check (page 32) develops the children's understanding that temperature is a measure of how hot things are and their knowledge of how to use a thermometer to make careful measurements of temperature, using standard units. Show the children how to

 When boiling water, ensure it is well away from the children, all of whom should be seated; protect your hand with a padded kitchen glove while taking the temperature of boiling water.

handle a thermometer safely and carefully, pointing out that it should be taken out of its protective tube before use (many children do not realise this). The thermometer should be returned to its tube after each use. A useful way of protecting thermometers in frequent use during a lesson is to fix a piece of sticky tape onto the table top to hold the thermometer. Ask the children to look at the scale on the thermometer, tell them that it is marked in degrees and that degrees are units for measuring heat, just as centimetres are units for measuring length. Note that these are degrees Celsius (named after the inventor of the Centigrade scale). Ask the children to place the thermometer on a table top and read the temperature indicated on it. Point out that this is the temperature of the air in the room. Ask them what happens to the temperature reading when they hold the bulb of the thermometer in their hand. What number on the scale does the liquid in the thermometer tube reach? Write up the temperature reading, showing the children the degrees symbol (°). Give the children a pot of ice and show them how to use the thermometer to take its temperature; point out that the thermometer needs to be left in it for about a minute, and that when they take the reading the bulb should still be in the ice. The temperature of the ice should be 0 °Celsius and the boiling water 100 °Celsius. For some children it will be enough to recognise that the level of the liquid in the thermometer rises as it becomes hotter and sinks as it becomes colder. You could link this with mathematics (numbers below zero).

Resources: laboratory thermometers with a scale of −10 to 110 °Celsius • five plastic pots or beakers

Vocabulary: *boiling, Celsius, degree, lukewarm, scale, temperature, thermometer.*

In **Temperature change** (page 33) the children will begin to develop an understanding that materials warm up or cool down until they are the same temperature as their surroundings, and an ability to explain both temperature and temperature changes through the use of scientific knowledge and

 When boiling water, ensure it is well away from the children, all of whom should be seated; protect your hand with a padded kitchen glove while taking the temperature of boiling water.

understanding. The activity should be carried out on a day when the children can check their predictions the following day. Most children will realise that an ice cube will melt if left in the classroom; it is important that they realise that it melts because it becomes warmer. Most children will also realise that cold water will become warmer and that hot water will cool down. Discuss the children's predictions for the changed temperature of each pot of water: are their predicted temperatures of ice and cold water higher than the starting temperature and are those of hot and boiling water lower? After the children have completed the activity discuss what makes the temperatures change and show the

children how to use a room thermometer to take the temperature of the air in the classroom. The temperature of all the pots of water and ice should now be about the same as the room temperature. Encourage the children to use appropriate spelling strategies for difficult words such as *thermometer, temperature* and *Celsius.*

Resources: laboratory thermometers with a scale of −10 to 110 °Celsius • a room thermometer with a scale of −10 to 50 °Celsius • five plastic pots or beakers

Vocabulary: *boil, boiling, Celsius, degree, freezing, frozen, lukewarm, melt, scale, temperature, thermometer.*

Hot spots (page 34) develops the children's ability to use either a room thermometer or a sensor attached to a computer to measure temperatures, to collect and store information and to explain their findings using their scientific knowledge and understanding. Show the children a room thermometer and a laboratory thermometer (which they should already have used) and ask them how the room thermometer is different. Can they explain why its scale finishes at 50 °C? They could take the temperature of the air in high places by fixing a thermometer to a long pole using elastic bands or sticky tape. Afterwards, ask the children why they think the air was colder in some places than others. If a heat sensor is available the children could record the temperature in specific places and present them in the form of a graph. If a temperature sensor linked to a PC is not available, the children can use a computer program to generate a graph of the temperatures. Discuss what causes the differences in temperature: for example, draughts under doors or through windows, heat from radiators. You could also explain that warm air is lighter than cold air and so rises above it.

Resources: laboratory thermometers with a scale of −10 to 110 °Celsius • room thermometers with a scale of −10 to 50 °Celsius

Vocabulary: *Celsius, cold, colder, cool, cooler, degree, sensor, temperature, thermometer, warm, warmer.*

Keep it warm (page 35) develops the children's skills in turning ideas about how to keep things warm into a form that can be investigated, and in deciding what evidence to collect. Wrapping a container of hot water in an insulating material (one that does not easily conduct heat) helps to prevent heat loss from the water to the air in the room (which is cooler than the water). Heat moves from warmer to cooler materials. One way to find out which materials are best for keeping hot water hot is to put the same amount of water, of the same temperature, in each of five cans and to record the starting temperature. Four cans can be wrapped in different materials (using the same thickness of material) and one, unwrapped, can be kept as a 'control' for comparison. The temperature of the water should be measured and recorded at intervals of about 10 or 15 minutes; or heat sensors, attached to a computer, can be used to record the temperature of the water in each can. Link this with literacy work on comparative adjectives: *warmer, cooler* and so on.

Resources: laboratory thermometers with a scale of −10 to 110 °Celsius • bubble wrap • fur fabric • kitchen foil • newspaper • drinks cans

Stop it melting (page 36) develops the children's understanding about insulators. Explore their ideas about why they think certain materials will be better than others for keeping the ice cube cold. Many children think that fur fabric will make the ice melt 'because it is warm'. They learn that the same materials that keep things warm also keep them cool: this time the materials stop the warmer air in the classroom losing heat to the cooler ice cube.

Resources: laboratory thermometers with a scale of −10 to 110 °Celsius • bubble wrap • fur fabric • kitchen foil • newspaper • plastic pots • ice cubes

Insulators (page 37) helps the children to learn about materials that are good thermal insulators: the same materials are good for keeping cold things cold as well as warm things warm. The children should notice that these good insulators feel warm: this is because they do not easily conduct heat from the skin. Polystyrene feels very warm, but the centre of a large block of this material is usually colder than its surroundings because it takes a long time to warm up. Introduce the term *insulator*.

Resources: fur fabric • kitchen foil • newspaper • polystyrene pieces • polythene

Conductors (page 38) demonstrates that wood and plastics are good thermal insulators but metals are not: the handle of the metal spoon

Hot water should not be uncomfortably hot.

will become hot if it is standing in hot water (or cold, if it is standing in ice) before the plastic or wooden one. Discuss the terms *conductor* and *insulator* and ask the children if they have heard them before in connection with science. Remind them about electrical conductors and insulators. They should notice that materials that are good thermal insulators are also good electrical insulators and that good thermal conductors are also good conductors of electricity.

Resources: two plastic pots • hot water • ice cubes • long-handled metal, plastic and wooden spoons

Hot and cold quiz (page 39) helps the children to recognise the different uses of thermal insulators and conductors. You could also discuss the use of clothing to keep us warm: the same type of material does not keep us cool when the weather is hot – unlike the insulation for hot drinks and ice cubes. This is because humans, like many other animals, generate heat energy. In order to keep cool, this heat has to be allowed to pass from the body to the surrounding air. Link the vocabulary with

literacy work on suffixes: *-or* in *conductor/insulator, -al* in *thermal.*

Solids, liquids and how they can be separated

All sorts of solids (page 40) reviews the children's understanding of the term *solid*. Some children might first need to practise grouping materials as 'solids' and 'liquids' and saying how solids differ from liquids. They are asked to group some solids using their own criteria and then to explain how they grouped them. After the children have completed the activity invite one of them to copy his or her groupings (without the notes) onto a whiteboard; ask the others if they can tell how the materials have been grouped. Ask the volunteer to explain the grouping and the others to check that the objects in each group match the criteria.

Resources: magnifying glasses • flour • gravel • modelling clay (soft) • Plasticine • rubber (for instance, an eraser) • salt • sand • stones • sugar • talcum powder • small blocks of wood

Solid or liquid? (page 41) reviews the children's understanding of the terms *solid* and *liquid*. After they have completed the activity, provide them with a collection of materials to classify as solid or liquid: powder paint, a thin mixture and a thick mixture of powder paint and water, washing powder, a thin and a thick mixture of washing powder and water, a glue stick, a viscous liquid glue, a thin liquid glue, sand. Discuss how they can tell if a material is solid or liquid: what do solids do that is different from liquids? Draw out the following: solids keep their shape without a container to hold them; liquids do not; liquids can be poured. The children might notice that some solids can be poured and do not keep their shapes without a container: for example, salt and powder paint. Point out that each small piece keeps its shape, and compare these solids with a bucket of stones or a skip-load of bricks: both of these can be 'poured' if something can lift them high enough. Sand and powder paint are the same but on a smaller scale. Some materials, such as jam, honey and yogurt, are difficult to class as solid or liquid. Encourage the children to apply the criteria you have discussed: 'Can it be poured?' 'Does it keep its shape without a container?' You could introduce the term *viscosity* to refer to the thickness of liquids.

Resources: powder paint • washing powder • water • a glue stick • a viscous liquid glue • a thin liquid glue • sand

Volume check (page 42) develops the children's skills in making careful observations and measurements of volume, recording them in tables and using them to draw conclusions. After the children have completed the activity, show them a collection of containers of different shapes that hold exactly one litre: for example, lemonade bottles, spring water bottles, ice cream boxes or tubs, fabric conditioner containers and cartons, a measuring jug, a measuring cylinder. Ask the children if they think the containers hold the same amount or if some hold more or less than others. Let them check their ideas by pouring water from one container to another.

Resources: six containers of similar (but not the same) volume • a collection of containers that hold one litre

Vocabulary: *capacity, liquid, litre, millilitre, volume.*

Bits and pieces (page 43) explores the idea that solids consisting of very small, but visible, pieces behave like liquids in some ways and draws out the essential differences between solids and liquids. Solids cannot be soaked up by a cloth or sponge because, unlike liquids, they are not drawn into the cavities in these porous materials by capillary action. Solids keep their shape without a container but liquids do not (see the notes for page 41). To link with literacy, focus on words ending in *-id*, such as *solid* and *liquid*. Challenge the children to think of others.

Resources: measuring jug • bowl or basin • sieve • absorbent cloth • sponge • small paper bag • salt • sand • sugar • washing-up liquid • water

Vocabulary: *grain, liquid, pour, shape, solid.*

Changes (page 44) explores changes of state: solid to liquid and liquid to solid. Draw out the idea that some solids (such as paper and sand) will not melt and that some (such as steel and other metals) do not melt easily. If the children have marked steel as a material that cannot be melted, discuss how they know (they might have seen steel saucepans, which do not melt). Establish that steel and many other metals melt at very high temperatures – much higher than those of an oven or a hob. Discuss the children's ideas for changing solids to liquids and vice versa; they could try those that are safe during another lesson. Butter, chocolate and candle wax can be melted in small plastic bags placed in hot water, or in small pots placed on a radiator. The liquids can be left in a freezer overnight and observed the next day.

Vocabulary: *freeze, liquid, melt, solid, solidify.*

Meltdown (page 45) is about the melting points of different solids. Some children might need to be reminded that *melting* means changing from solid to liquid. The children could check some solids practically: for example, butter, beeswax, chocolate, ice, ice cream and margarine. Use a gentle form of heat (see the notes for page 44). A thermometer should be left in the materials while they melt. Note that the temperature stays the same throughout the melting process. This could be shown by making a line graph on which to record the temperature of the melting material at five-minute intervals.
Answers: gold 1064 °C, lead 216 °C, polyethylene 100–130 °C, beeswax 62–65 °C, chocolate 20 °C, butter 12 °C, margarine 10 °C, ice 0 °C, ice cream –6 °C.
Tell the children these temperatures if they cannot find them in other sources, discuss their implications in everyday life, and set questions for them to investigate: for example, 'Would lead be a good material for cookers and pans?', 'Why does chocolate melt in our hands?', 'Why can we spread margarine straight from the fridge but not butter?', 'Why do we need to keep ice cream in a freezer, rather than in a fridge?'

Vocabulary: *liquid, melt, solid, temperature, thermometer.*

Sieve it (page 46) develops the children's understanding of which mixtures of materials can be separated mechanically. They should be able to use sieves of different grades to separate the largest pieces and then the smaller ones. They should notice that materials consisting of similar-sized pieces cannot be separated using a sieve. Children who undertake the extension activity should think about materials with much smaller holes than sieves; for example, cloth and tissue paper.

Resources: finely-graded and coarsely-graded sieves • dried peas • sand • salt • sugar • paper clips • flour

Vocabulary: *graded, mixture, separate, sieve.*

The mad mixer (page 47) focuses on the ways materials behave when mixed with water: dissolving/not dissolving, changing the colour of the water, fizzing and combining with the water to form a solid. The children should notice that a mixture of plaster of Paris and water becomes hot as it solidifies: this is because heat is produced during the reaction between the plaster and the water. The plaster cannot be separated from the water. Baking powder also reacts with water to produce a gas: that is why it fizzes; it cannot be separated from the water, although some solid material can be filtered out. Flour mixes with water to form a new material.

Resources: plastic pots • spoons • baking powder • beads • powdered chalk • instant coffee • plain flour • plaster of Paris • salt • sand • sugar • water

Vocabulary: *dissolve, mixture, react.*

Sieve and filter (page 48) draws on the children's learning about sieving and about materials that dissolve in water. They should notice that only materials that do not dissolve can be filtered out of water. Instant coffee dissolves in water if the water is warm enough but ground coffee does not.

Vocabulary: *dissolve, filter, mixture, separate, sieve.*

Solutions (page 49) consolidates the children's learning about solutions and develops their understanding that a dissolved solid such as sugar or salt is still present even though it cannot be seen and that dissolved solids cannot be separated from water by sieving or filtering. Discuss the children's everyday experience of

 Utensils used for tasting or for preparing food should not be used for other purposes; all equipment should be sterilised before use and the children should wash their hands before beginning the activity.

dissolving: for example, sugar in hot drinks. How can they tell if there is sugar in a drink? They can taste the sugar and salt solutions to check if the salt or sugar is still present, and the filtered liquid to see if it has been filtered out.

Resources: beakers • spoons • water • salt • sugar • coffee

Vocabulary: *dissolve, filter, separate, sieve, solution.*

Friction

Forcemeters (page 50) demonstrates how to measure forces and introduces the *newton* as the unit of force. Before beginning the activity you could ask the children to use information books, CD-ROMs and the Internet to find out about Isaac Newton, the first scientist to identify the force of gravity, after whom the unit of force is named. Note that, although the unit *newton* is written in lower-case letters, for the abbreviation a capital letter is used (*N*). Forcemeters (sometimes called *newton meters* or *spring balances*) are available in different scales: for example, 0–15N, 0–25N, 0–50N, 0–100N, 0–500N and 0–1000N. To create these different scales on forcemeters of similar sizes, different strengths of spring are used. If necessary, let the children explore the differences between forcemeters with different scales by gently pulling against the springs. Point out that over extending the springs damages the mechanism. The weight of an object is measured by the pull of the Earth's gravity on it; weight is measured in newtons (mass is measured in grams). A newton is defined as the amount of force that would make a mass of 1 kg speed up by 1 metre per second, every second. In everyday language we say that an object has a *weight* of, say, 2 kg, but it is more accurate to say that it has a *mass* of 2 kg and a *weight* (on Earth) of about 20N. On Earth 1 kg weighs 10N. It would have a different weight on the Moon or on another planet, depending on the force of gravity.

Resources: forcemeters with different scales • small plastic bags to hang from a hook • a large stone • a shoe • a brick

Vocabulary: *force, forcemeter, gram, gravity, kilogram, newton, newton meter, pull, scale, spring balance.*

Surface test (page 51) provides an opportunity for the children to put into practice what they have learned about forcemeters as they investigate the forces needed to move a brick on different surfaces. A force is needed only to start an object moving; no force is needed to keep it moving but a force (such as friction) may act against it. Introduce the word *friction*. The children should change only the floor surface and keep the brick the same and ensure that the surface is always level. After the children have planned their investigations, discuss their ideas and provide an opportunity for them to carry them out and record their results. Did the results answer their question? How well? Is there anything else they need to do in order to find the answer?

Resources: forcemeters • carpet • concrete surface • vinyl floor surface • rubber mat • brick • string

Vocabulary: *force, forcemeter, friction, newton, pull, rough, smooth, surface.*

In **Safe shoes** (page 52) the children learn about friction between the soles of shoes and a floor surface. Discuss when this is useful (for example, for sports and for walking on snow and ice or on the decks of boats) and when a weaker force of friction is suitable (for example, in dancing, when the feet sometimes need to slide slightly). Point out that in the investigation the higher the plank has to be raised in order to make the shoe move, the greater the grip the shoe has.

Vocabulary: *force, friction, grip, rough, slide, smooth.*

Friction (page 53) focuses on the difference between the forces of friction acting between different pairs of surfaces. The children should find that a rough surface does not necessarily cause a strong force of friction if the object moving along it is smooth. To link with literacy, ask the children to make a rhyme-bank for the word *friction*.

Resources: bricks • forcemeters • string • polythene bag • woollen cloth • nylon cloth • rubber sheeting • carpet • vinyl floor • rubber mat (for example, a car mat)

Vocabulary: *force, forcemeter, friction, grip, newton, slide.*

ICT In **Dive bombers** (page 54) the children explore water resistance and learn that it slows an object moving through water. From the results of the investigation they are asked to identify trends, draw conclusions, and explain these conclusions in terms of the force between the object and the water. Ask the children if they have ever walked through deep water. They could try this in a swimming lesson. How does it compare with walking on dry land? Ask them what they are walking through on land (air). Which is easier to walk through – air or water? Ask the children if a ball of Plasticine will move more quickly through air than through water. They could check their predictions by comparison rather than by measuring the time taken (the Plasticine will fall through the air too quickly to be timed). Ask them what makes the Plasticine fall more slowly through water than through air. Some children might find the investigation easier if they drop all the Plasticine shapes into separate cylinders of water at the same time and observe the order in which they reach the bottom. Discuss the results of the comparison of the different Plasticine shapes. Why should some shapes fall more quickly than others? The children should notice that the narrower the shape, particularly at the leading end, the faster it falls. This is because it has a smaller surface against which the force of the water (water resistance) can act. They could look for other streamlined shapes that move through water in real-life situations: motor boats, people diving, ducks and other birds diving. A complementary activity for this sheet is available on the website (see Year 4 Activity 4).

Resources: tall measuring cylinder • Plasticine • stopwatch or timer

Vocabulary: *force, streamlined, water resistance.*

Speed boats (page 55) explores the effect of water resistance in a horizontal direction. The children should use what they have learned from their previous work to predict which boat will be the fastest.

Resources: a long shallow plant tray containing water • a stopwatch or timer • a small battery-operated fan • boats with different-shaped hulls (the boats' hulls can be cut from softwood: using a drill bit of the same diameter as the mast, drill a hole into which to fix a mast made from a rounded lollipop stick or piece of thin dowel; if the boat is top-heavy, weight the hull with Plasticine)

Vocabulary: *hull, streamlined, water resistance.*

Free fall (page 56) examines the effects of air resistance on objects moving downwards. Point out that air resistance, like water resistance, is a force that acts in all directions against objects moving through it. Ask the children to explain why certain shapes fall more quickly than others. The greater the surface area of the shape, the greater the area against which air resistance can act and so the greater the force against which the object has to move.

Resources: Plasticine • paper

> **Vocabulary:** *air resistance, force, surface area.*

For **Time for a challenge** (page 57) the children could work in pairs on their designs. Discuss the idea of an optimum size of feathers or parachute. The children need to drop the corks from a height to be able to make out any significant differences between the times they take to fall.

 Close supervision is needed if the children drop the corks over a stairwell or from a high surface such as a platform or table top.

> **Vocabulary:** *air resistance, surface area.*

Circuits and conductors

 Circuit check (page 58) reviews the children's understanding of what is needed to make an electrical circuit work: it needs a power source and must be unbroken. The children could explain the purpose of each part of the circuit: the battery gives it power/energy/electricity; the bulb turns this energy into light; the wire connects the bulb to the battery. Allow the children to make the circuits to check their answers. A complementary activity for this sheet is available on the website (see Year 4 Activity 5).

Resources: 1.5 volt batteries • bulbs • bulb-holders • wire (with the ends stripped)

> **Vocabulary:** *battery, circuit, electricity.*

Electrical conductors (page 59) consolidates the children's understanding that an electrical circuit has to be made of metal; it introduces the term *conductors* for materials that allow electricity to pass through them and shows

 Remind the children that it is safe to experiment with circuits powered by batteries but not with mains electricity.

that metals are the best conductors. If the children have previously made circuits using only a bulb, battery and wire, let them examine a bulb-holder to follow the path of the electrical circuit:

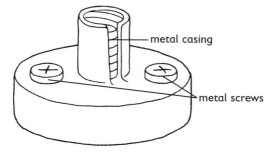

Underneath the base a metal strip links the metal end of one screw to the metal casing inside the bulb-holder. The other screw is linked to a strip of metal leading to the base of the bulb.

Also let them examine a battery-holder so that they can see how the wires of a battery snap are joined to each terminal of the battery:

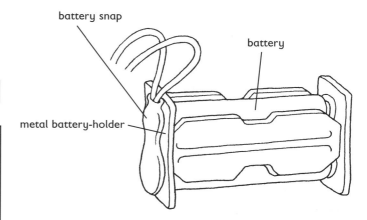

Discuss electrical safety. Point out that it is safe to handle bare wires in a circuit powered by a battery but not one powered by mains electricity. Ask the children to read the voltage marked on the batteries (1.5V); point out that the voltage of mains electricity is 220 to 240 volts. You could tell them that the *volt* is a unit of measure for the power provided by a source of electricity and that it was named after the Italian scientist Alessandro Volta. At another time they could use information books, CD-ROMs or the Internet to find out more about Volta. Note that *volt* is written in lower-case but its abbreviation is upper-case (*V*). After the children have completed the activity, ask them what they notice about the types of material that conduct electricity. Let them test any other available metals; for example, gold or silver jewellery, if any adults are wearing it (children usually enjoy using a gold ring, still on the owner's finger, as a conductor). Ask the children to notice which parts of the circuit are made of plastic, and ask them why they think metal is not used for the whole circuit. Relate this to mains electricity (you could show them an opened electrical plug). They should realise that plastic is used to stop electricity passing through some parts (for example, plastic-coated wires).

Resources: 1.5V batteries in battery-holders • 2.5V–3.5V bulbs in bulb-holders • crocodile clips • wire • samples of metals, including aluminium, lead and steel • pieces of charcoal, leather, paper, plastic, wood and woollen cloth

> **Vocabulary:** *battery, battery-holder, bulb, bulb-holder, circuit, conductor, crocodile clip, insulator, wire.*

Circuit fun (page 60) consolidates the children's learning about conductors and insulators. Circuits A and B will work because all the objects used to link the bulb to the battery are made of metal.

 Explain how insulators are used in mains electricity; for example, rubber and plastic coating for wire, plastic covers for plugs and sockets.

Resources: 1.5V batteries in battery-holders • battery snaps • 2.5V–3.5V bulbs in bulb-holders • wire • bulldog clips • metal foil • nails • paper clips • pens • plastic and metal spoons

> **Vocabulary:** *battery, battery-holder, bulb, bulb-holder, circuit, conductor, crocodile clip, insulator, wire.*

On and off (page 61) develops the children's understanding of how switches work in electrical circuits. There are several ways in which they can make a switch:

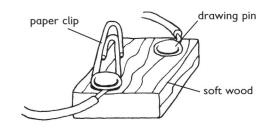

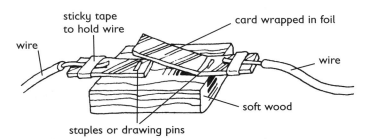

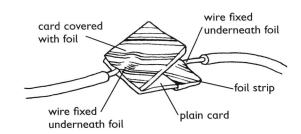

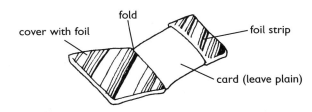

Resources: 1.5V batteries in battery-holders • battery snaps • 2.5V–3.5V bulbs in bulb-holders • wire • small pieces of soft wood • paper clips • drawing pins • kitchen foil • card • a disconnected mains plug

Vocabulary: *battery, battery-holder, bulb, bulb-holder, circuit, conductor, switch, wire.*

Extra power (page 62) demonstrates the need to match power sources to electrical components. The children learn that if a bulb is under-powered it does not shine as brightly as it could; also that if it is given too much power it will burn out.

⚠️ Remind the children about the danger of mains electricity. Point out that it has a very high voltage (220–240V) compared with the low voltage of batteries (1.5–6V).

After the children have completed the activity, provide them with different types of bulbs and batteries and ask them to read the voltages marked on them (using a magnifying glass, if necessary). The figure indicates the voltage required to make the bulb shine as brightly as intended. Point out that a battery should be matched to the voltage of the bulb. Remind the children about the voltage of mains electricity and ensure they understand that it would be very dangerous to connect the small bulbs they have been using to a mains supply. To link with literacy, explore nouns made by adding the suffix *-age*: *voltage, mileage* and so on.

Resources: 1.5V batteries • 2.5V–6V bulbs in bulb-holders • wire

Vocabulary: *battery, bulb, bulb-holder, circuit, electricity, energy, power, volt, voltage, wire.*

Extra bulbs (page 63) shows children how to connect bulbs in series. Some children might need help with making the test fair. When using layers of paper as a home-made light-meter, ask them to think about the type of paper used and the distance between the paper and the bulb. Each time a bulb is added to a series circuit the bulbs become dimmer because the resistance in the circuit is increased. This diagram explains resistance by comparing the electrical current with water flowing through pipes:

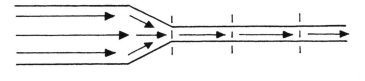

series (3 bulbs represented by grilles)

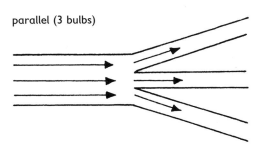

parallel (3 bulbs)

It is not necessary to explain resistance to the children, unless their questions indicate that this is appropriate.

Resources: 1.5V batteries in battery-holders • 2.5V–3.5V bulbs in bulb-holders • wire

Vocabulary: *battery, bulb, bulb-holder, circuit, electricity, energy, power, volt, voltage, wire.*

Speed it up (page 64) demonstrates how to connect a motor to an electrical circuit. Children learn that, like a bulb, a motor needs the correct voltage of battery to make it work properly. Remind them about what happens to bulbs given too high a voltage (they burn out); point out that this can happen to a motor, too. The children who undertake the extension activity could measure the speed of the motor by counting the turns of the propeller. Challenge them to find a way to count when the propeller turns too fast for them to make out each turn. They could attach a longer piece of plastic to it that could tap a piece of card or metal. They could count the taps they hear.

Resources: 1.5V batteries • battery-holders • motors • propellers • sticky tape • wire

Vocabulary: *battery, bulb, bulb-holder, circuit, electricity, energy, power, volt, voltage, wire.*

Review knowledge of bones

- **Draw the** bones .
- **Label any you know.**

Dem bones
dem bones –
Dem dry bones ...

- **Check: feel your own bones.**

  Have you missed any on the picture?

Now try this!

- **Write about your bones:**

  Where can you feel them?

  What do they feel like?

- **See if you can count your** ribs **and the bones of your** spine .

Teachers' note Encourage the children to check (by feeling their own bones) how many bones they have and their shapes, where possible: for example, in their arms, legs, hands, feet, back and chest. After completing the activity the children could make a life-sized display of a skeleton. Some of them could draw round the outline of one of the class on black paper and cut it out. The whole class could draw and cut out bones from white paper and glue them onto it.

Developing Science
Year 4
© A & C BLACK

Whose skeleton? **ICT**

Understand that some animals have bony skeletons

Which animals' | skeletons | are these?

• **Write the names.**

[ ]

[ ]

[ ]

[ ]

[ ]

• **Compare two of the skeletons:**

[ ] and [ ]

Similarities	Differences

Now try this!

How does each animal's skeleton help it to move?

Use information books, CD-ROMs and websites.

Teachers' note Show the children pictures of animals such as a dog, a cat, an elephant, a giraffe, a swan and an alligator. Ask them what they think the animals' skeletons are like. They could copy or trace outlines of the animals onto black paper, cut them out and on them make chalk drawings of what they think their skeletons look like. Ask them to look at the pictures of skeletons on this page and to imagine them with flesh and skin on them. They could use pictures to help.

Developing Science
Year 4
© A & C BLACK

Our growing bones

Salim and Tracy were finding out about | bones |.

Here is a question they wanted to answer:

Do Year 4 children have longer forearms than Year 1 children?

forearm

- **Read what Salim and Tracy planned to do:**

We shall measure our forearms, then we shall measure Salim's sister Fawzia's forearm because she is in Year 1. We shall see if our forearms are longer than Fawzia's.

How can Salim and Tracy's plan be improved?

- **Write what you would do.**

_____
_____
_____
_____
_____
_____
_____

What would you expect to find out? _____

_____

Now try this!

- **Think about the growth of bones in** | the head | | the feet | | the legs |.
- **Write a question to investigate.**

Teachers' note Ask the children to feel particular bones in their bodies: the bones in their forearms, the tops of their arms, their skull, upper and lower leg and so on. Name a bone and ask them if they think theirs or an adult's is bigger and how they know. Read the introductory information on this page, including Salim and Tracy's question and how they plan to find the answer. What is good about the plan and what could be done to improve it?

Developing Science
Year 4
© **A & C BLACK**

A bony question

Sarah and Leo's question:

Do Year 6 children have bigger skulls than Year 3 children?

What they will do

Measure the distance round the heads of 10 Year 6 and 10 Year 3 children (5 boys and 5 girls). Measure them all in the same place (just above the eyes).

- **Predict: what will they find out, and why?** _____

_____

- **Investigate Sarah and Leo's question and record your findings on two bar charts:**

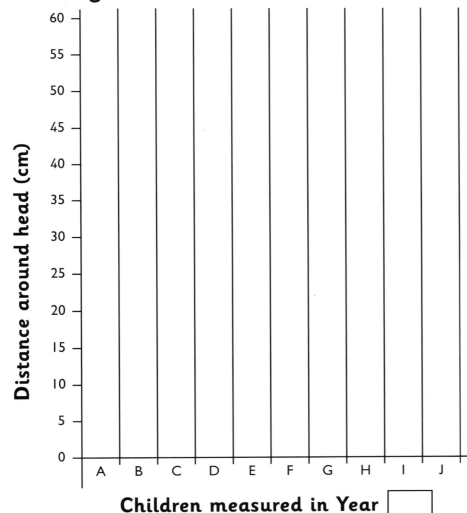

Distance around head (cm)

| 60 | 55 | 50 | 45 | 40 | 35 | 30 | 25 | 20 | 15 | 10 | 5 | 0 |

A B C D E F G H I J

Children measured in Year ☐

Make two copies of this graph before you begin, one for each year.

To save space give each child a letter.

Teachers' note The children should first have completed page 16. Read Sarah and Leo's plan and discuss what makes it better than Salim and Tracy's. They should measure round the heads of the children in Year 3, as shown, and record each one on the bar chart. Repeat this for Year 6. You could delete or change the letters below the horizontal axis. They have been provided for guidance.

**Developing Science
Year 4**
© **A & C BLACK**

Look – no bones!

Understand that the skeleton supports the body

Humans are ⬚vertebrates⬚: they have a backbone that is part of a hard skeleton inside their bodies. Some animals do not have this kind of skeleton. They are called ⬚invertebrates⬚.

• **Write** ⬚vertebrate⬚ **or** ⬚invertebrate⬚ **for each animal.**

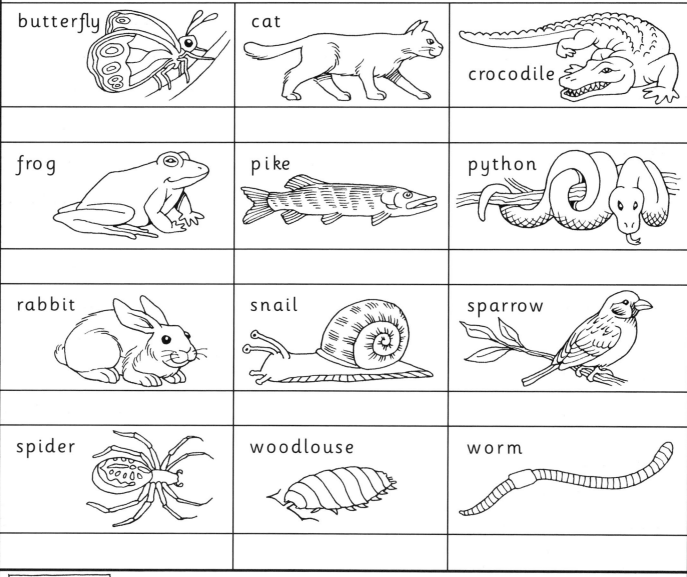

butterfly	cat	crocodile
frog	pike	python
rabbit	snail	sparrow
spider	woodlouse	worm

Now try this!

• **Find out what a skeleton is for. What do invertebrates have instead?**

Use information books.

Teachers' note Provide animals for the children to observe (see page 5) and pictures of other animals they cannot observe in real life. Ask them to identify those with a skeleton inside their bodies and a backbone, like humans. What is the skeleton for? What would happen to the body if it had no skeleton? Which animals do not have a skeleton inside their bodies? How are their bodies supported? Point out the tough skin.

Developing Science Year 4 © A & C BLACK

Phew!

Recognise that during exercise the muscles work hard

- ## Record your observations about your body:
  - ## when you are resting
  - ## when you are exercising.

What to observe	Resting	Exercising
breathing		
heartbeat		
how you feel		
what happens to your skin		
temperature		

Now try this!

- ## Find out why these changes happen to your body when you exercise.
- ## Write a report.

Use information books, CD–ROMs and the Internet.

Teachers' note During a PE lesson ask the children to observe how their bodies change when they exercise: muscles work harder during exercise than during sitting or standing still. Explain that muscles use energy when they work and that the body works hard to provide this energy; relate this to changes the children observe: faster heart beat and breathing. The children might notice other changes, such as feeling hotter, sweating, a redder skin colour.

**Developing Science
Year 4
© A & C BLACK**

Is it alive?

- **List the things in the picture that are** alive .
- **List the things that are** not alive .

Alive	Not alive

Now try this!

- **Choose something that is alive and something that is not alive.**
- **Explain how you can tell if it is alive or not alive.**

Teachers' note Take the children for a walk around the school and its surroundings to look for living things. Point out difficult examples such as seeds, fruits and leaves that have fallen off plants; cut grass; feathers, animal hair or wool; dead animals (insects, spiders, woodlice and worms can often be found). Show the children a burning candle, an eggshell and a torch and ask them if they are alive. Discuss their responses (see page 6).

**Developing Science
Year 4**
© A & C BLACK

Plant or animal?

Review the terms *plant* and *animal*

Most living organisms are | plants | **or** | animals | .
Which are these? ✔
How can you tell?

> Think about what the organisms need and what they can do.

	plant ☐		plant ☐
	animal ☐		animal ☐
sycamore		robin	

Reason:

Reason:

	plant ☐		plant ☐
	animal ☐		animal ☐
spider		grass	

Reason:

Reason:

	plant ☐		plant ☐
	animal ☐		animal ☐
lizard		bat	

Reason:

Reason:

Now try this!

- **List the ways in which one of the animals above is like you.**

Teachers' note Ideally, the children should first have completed page 20. Remind them that humans are animals, show them other animals that can be brought into school (or pictures of animals) and ask them how they can tell that these are animals. In what ways are they like people? Show them some plants and ask them in what ways they are like and unlike animals. After completing the activity the children could write definitions of plants and animals.

**Developing Science
Year 4
© A & C BLACK**

A place to live

Recognise that different animals are suited to different habitats

What organisms might you find in the habitats below, and why?

- Complete the chart.

Habitat	Conditions (damp, dry, wet, dark, light, sheltered, exposed)	Organisms (animal and plant)	Reasons
under a stone			
a patch of grass			
a wall			
an oak tree			

- List any other conditions you have noticed in a habitat.

Developing Science
Year 4
© A & C BLACK

Teachers' note Discuss local habitats that are familiar to the children. What conditions do these habitats have? The children should say if a habitat is damp, wet, dry, dark, light, sheltered or exposed. Ask them what living things they expect to find in each habitat, and why.

22

Groups

- ## Cut out the pictures and put the organisms into groups.
- ## Make notes about how you have grouped them.

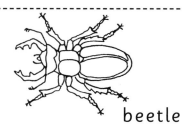

beetle

buttercup

cow

daisy

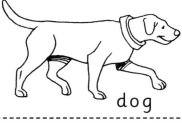

dog

fly

frog

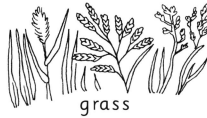

grass

horse

ladybird

lizard

oak

rabbit

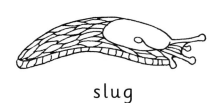

slug

snail

sycamore

willow

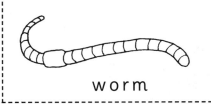

worm

Teachers' note The children should first have completed page 22 and had the opportunity to group organisms they have collected from a local habitat, such as part of the school grounds. Include animals and plants in the collection. Let the children group the organisms in their own ways and then ask them to explain their groupings. They could compare this with the groupings made by others.

Developing Science
Year 4
© A & C BLACK

Keys: 1

Use keys to identify local animals

beetle

earthworm

snail

spider

wasp

woodlouse

Write a question to split the animals into two sets. The answer must be ☐ yes ☐ or ☐ no ☐.

_____

Write the names of the animals.

Yes   **No**

Write a question to split this group into two.

_____
_____

Yes   **No**

Write a question to split this group into two.

_____
_____

Yes   **No**

Now try this!

- **Continue writing questions until all the animals have been separated.**

Teachers' note Read the first part of this page with the children and help them to write suitable questions for splitting the groups of animals.

Developing Science
Year 4
© A & C BLACK

Keys: 2

Use keys to identify local plants

• Use the ⬚key⬚ to identify the trees.

A 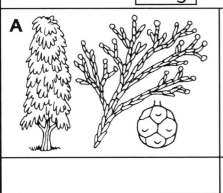	**B**  	**C** 
D 	**E** 	**F** 

Key

Does it have needles?

Yes → No

Yes: Does it have cones?

No: Does it have winged seeds?

Does it have cones? → Yes / No

Yes: Are the cones round?

No: yew

Are the cones round? → Yes / No

Yes: cypress

No: Norway spruce

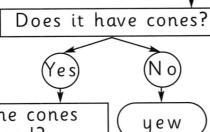

Does it have winged seeds? → Yes / No

Yes: sycamore

No: Are the fruits spiky?

Are the fruits spiky? → Yes / No

Yes: London plane

No: rowan

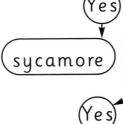
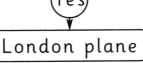

Now try this!

• **Collect six flowers whose names you know.**
• **Make a key to help someone else to identify them.**

Teachers' note The children should first have completed pages 23–24. Some children might find this easier if they cut out the pictures and then split them into two groups according to the answers to the questions. Some of them might be able to think of different questions and make a different key for identifying the plants in this collection.

**Developing Science
Year 4
© A & C BLACK**

Asking questions ICT

What could you find out about each animal?
• Write a question that you could investigate.

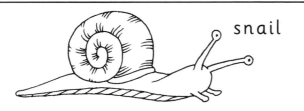 snail

My question:

_____

_____

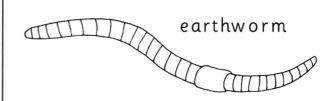 earthworm

My question:

_____

_____

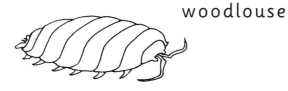 woodlouse

My question:

_____

_____

 starling

My question:

_____

_____

 gerbil

My question:

_____

_____

 goldfish

My question:

_____

_____

 Now try this!
• Discuss your questions with a friend.
• Make notes about how you could investigate one of them.

Teachers' note Remind the children of their previous learning about animals and encourage them to think of questions they can investigate by observing the animals. They could find out about the animals' bodies, how particular features help them to survive and why the animals act in particular ways.

Developing Science
Year 4
© A & C BLACK

Let's investigate

• **Use this page to plan an investigation about an animal.**

Our question:

What we shall do:

Taking care of the animal:

Our health and safety:

What we shall observe or measure:

What we expect to find out:

How we shall know the answer to our question:

Teachers' note The children should first have completed page 26. Help the children to select a suitable question to investigate (or go to page 28). The children could plan their investigations in groups. Different groups could carry out their investigations at different times and the results could be displayed for others to read.

Developing Science
Year 4
© **A & C BLACK**

27

What does it eat?

• **Plan an investigation to find out what an animal likes to eat.**

Animal: What we think it likes to eat:	How we shall keep the animal safe:
What we shall do:	How we shall look after our own health and safety:
How we shall make the test fair:	What we shall observe and record:
How we shall know what the animal likes to eat:	

Teachers' note Ideally, the children should first have completed page 27. They could choose an animal whose food preferences they can investigate: for example, a snail, a spider, a stick insect, a gerbil or a rabbit in a hutch. Discuss the types of food they will offer the animal and ensure that none can harm it. Ask the children how they can ensure that all foods have an equal chance of being eaten by the animal and how they will know which ones it prefers.

Developing Science
Year 4
© A & C BLACK

Look it up

Identify the food sources of different animals

- **Find out about the feeding habits of an animal you cannot observe.**

Use books, CD-ROMs and the Internet and write to people.

Animal _____

What I know	What I want to find out	Where I shall find out

Keep a note of book titles and pages, websites and pages and so on.

- **Write notes about your findings.**

Notes	Where I found out

- **Write a report about the animal.**

Now try this!

Teachers' note Provide pictures of animals the children cannot observe at first hand. Ask them if they know what the animal eats and how it gets its food. They should write the name of their chosen animal, fill in the section of the planning sheet headed *What I know* and then decide what else they would like to know about the animal's feeding habits. Encourage them to write as precisely as possible what sources they will use to find out.

Developing Science
Year 4
© A & C BLACK

Changing places

Recognise ways in which living things and the environment need protection

Which animals would survive? How?

What would happen if ...

... this pond were filled in?

dragonfly
frog
frogspawn
ducks
reedmace
waterlilies

... this oak tree were cut down?

sparrows in nest
robin
ladybird
squirrel
aphids
acorns

Now try this!

- **Find out about another** habitat **.**
- **Draw and describe it.**
- **What would happen if the habitat were changed?**

Teachers' note Begin by discussing a habitat the children have studied and whose food chains they know. Ask them what would happen if, for example, the roses in the school garden were sprayed to kill the greenfly. How would this affect the other animals in the food chain?

Developing Science
Year 4
© A & C BLACK

Feel the heat

- **Put your hands into the bowls of water:**

| Do not use water that is too hot to touch. |

right hand

left hand

very warm water

icy water

You need

bowl

bucket

very warm water

bowl

lukewarm water

icy water

- **After about a minute take your hands out of the water.**
- **Put them straight into a bucket of lukewarm water.**
- **Record what you feel.**

lukewarm water

Right hand	Left hand	Explanation
_____	_____	_____
_____	_____	_____
_____	_____	_____

- **Explain why touch is not a good way of judging how hot things are.**

_____

_____

_____

Now try this!

- **Find a way to test the water more accurately.**
- **Record your results on a chart.**

Teachers' note Provide each group of children with two bowls and a bucket of water as shown and point out that, for safety, the hot water is not too hot to put their hand into comfortably. Check that they know what *lukewarm* means. After they have completed the activity, ask them what made the same water feel hot to one hand but cool to the other. For the extension activity, ask the children what else they could use to measure how warm the water is.

Developing Science Year 4 © A & C BLACK

Temperature check

Use a thermometer to measure temperature

- **Use this page for recording the temperatures of ice, cold water, lukewarm water, hot water and boiling water.**

! An adult should take the temperature of boiling water.

Celsius

ice

cold water

lukewarm water

hot water

boiling water

110° 100° 90° 80° 70° 60° 50° 40° 30° 20° 10° 0° –10°

- **What do you think the temperature of the water will be if you mix equal amounts of ice and hot water?**
- **Find out.**

Now try this!

Teachers' note Begin by introducing the thermometer, what it is for and how to use it (see page 8). Ask the children to take the temperature of some ice and record it by colouring the appropriate diagram. Will cold water have a higher or lower temperature than ice? Ask the children to find out and record the temperature. Do the same with lukewarm and hot water and then ask them to predict the temperature of boiling water. Boil a kettle or pan of water and take its temperature yourself.

Developing Science
Year 4
© A & C BLACK

Temperature change

Understand that materials will warm up or cool down until they are the same temperature as their surroundings

Check the temperatures.

- **Measure the temperatures.**
- **Predict the** temperature changes **if the water is left in the classroom.**

New temperature

	Start temperature	After 1 hour		After 2 hours		After 24 hours	
		Predicted	Checked	Predicted	Checked	Predicted	Checked
ice							
cold water							
lukewarm water							
hot water							
boiling water ⚠							

Now try this!

What patterns do you notice in the temperature changes?

Teachers' note It would be helpful if the children have first completed pages 31 and 32. Remind the children of their previous work on ice cubes and ask them if they remember the temperature at which water freezes. Draw out the idea that as the temperature of the ice rises it becomes water and ask the children to predict the temperature to which it will rise if left in the classroom overnight. Ask them to measure the temperatures of cold water, lukewarm water, hot water and (an adult does this) boiling water, and to predict the temperatures they will have the next day.

Developing Science
Year 4
© A & C BLACK

Hot spots

Use IT to collect, store and retrieve data about temperatures

- **Measure the** temperature **in different parts of your classroom or school.**
- **Record your results on the thermometers:**

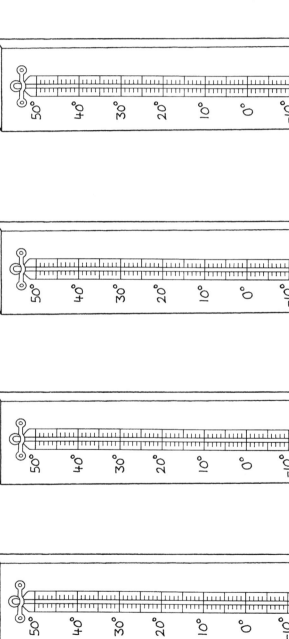

Celsius

Place

Teachers' note The children could use a thermometer or heat sensor attached to a computer to measure the temperature in different parts of the school or classroom. With the children, decide in which parts of the classroom to measure the air temperature. Encourage them to predict if any places will be cooler or warmer than others and to suggest reasons why.

Developing Science
Year 4
© A & C BLACK

Keep it warm

Plan a fair test to investigate how to keep things warm

Which material is the best for keeping things warm?

• **Plan an investigation using the materials shown.**

You need

drinks cans

thermometer

fur fabric

newspaper

bubble wrap

kitchen foil

clock

What I shall do:

Things I shall keep the same:

The one thing I shall change:

What I shall measure and record:

My prediction:

Teachers' note Ask the children how they think they could stop hot water from cooling down. Discuss some of the ways they know of keeping drinks warm and ask them if they think wrapping a container of hot water will make any difference. Different groups could try different materials for insulating the can. Ensure that they plan to keep a 'control' that is not wrapped and that they plan to measure the start and finish temperature of each one.

Developing Science
Year 4
© A & C BLACK

Stop it melting

• **Think of a way of stopping an ice cube from | melting | for as long as possible. What could you wrap round it?**

You cannot use a fridge or a freezer. The ice cube is in a small plastic bag.

What I shall do:	I need:

Why I think my idea will work:

How we can compare our ideas to find out which one worked best:

Teachers' note The children should first have completed page 35. Remind them what they have learned about temperature changes. To stop an ice cube melting, what must be done? Discuss some of the ways they know of keeping things cool and ask them if they think wrapping an ice cube will make any difference. Will the same materials that they used for keeping water hot be good for keeping ice cold?

Developing Science
Year 4
© A & C BLACK

Insulators

Recognise that some materials are good thermal insulators

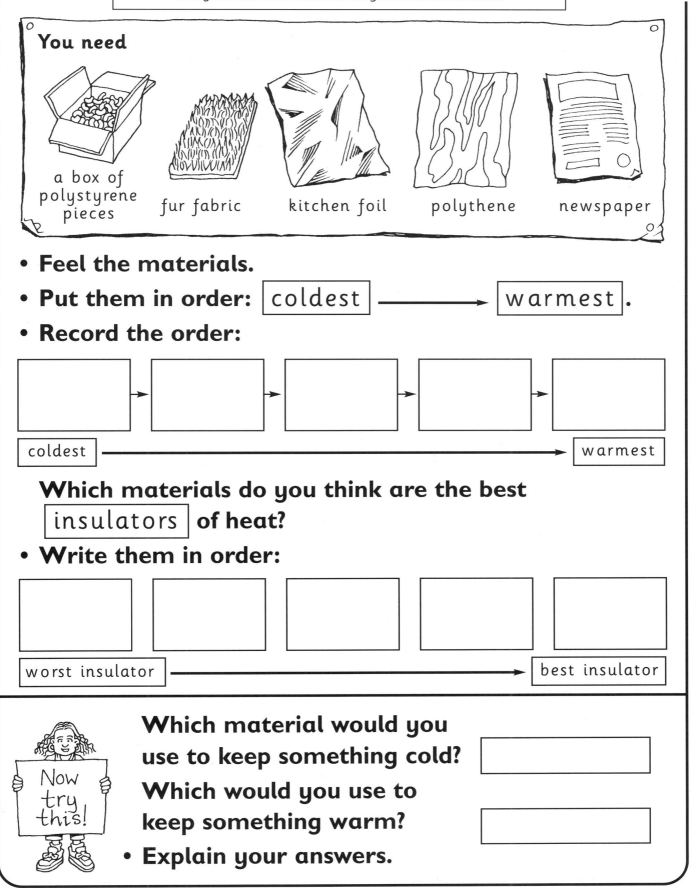

You need

a box of polystyrene pieces   fur fabric   kitchen foil   polythene   newspaper

- **Feel the materials.**
- **Put them in order:** coldest ⟶ warmest .
- **Record the order:**

coldest ⟶ warmest

Which materials do you think are the best insulators **of heat?**

- **Write them in order:**

worst insulator ⟶ best insulator

Which material would you use to keep something cold?

Which would you use to keep something warm?

- **Explain your answers.**

Now try this!

Teachers' note The children should first have completed pages 35 and 36. Discuss what they have learned about the materials that kept hot water the warmest and were best for keeping ice cool. What do they notice about the feel of these materials? They should notice that materials that feel warm are good insulators.

Developing Science
Year 4
© A & C BLACK

Conductors

Recognise that metals are not good thermal insulators but that wood and plastics are

How will the tip of each spoon's handle feel?

• **Write in the boxes.**

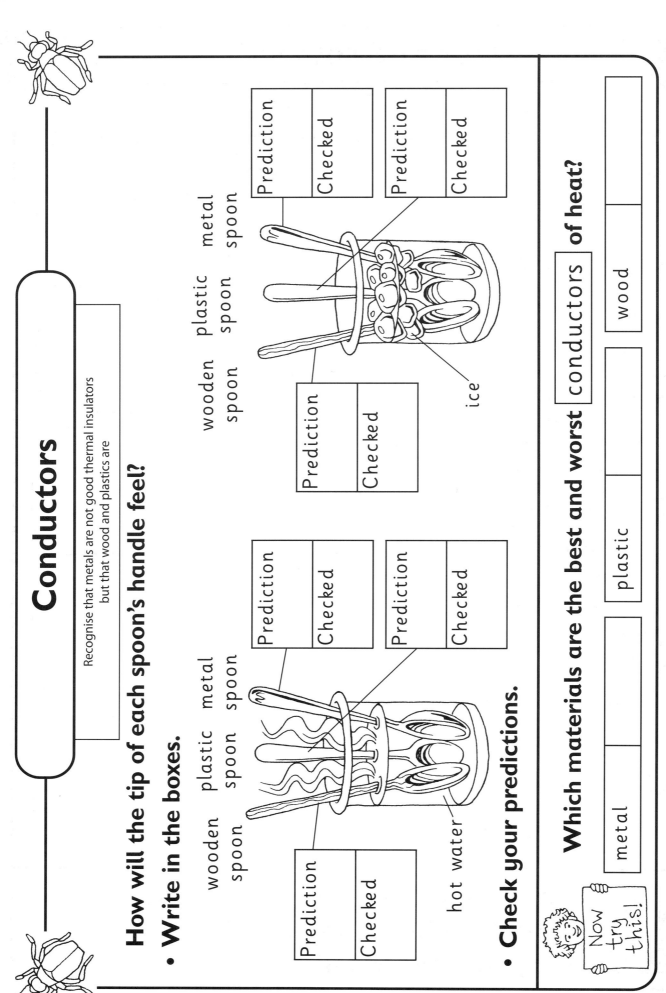

wooden spoon   plastic spoon   metal spoon

| Prediction |
| Checked |

| Prediction |
| Checked |

| Prediction |
| Checked |

| Prediction |
| Checked |

| Prediction |
| Checked |

hot water

wooden spoon   plastic spoon   metal spoon

| Prediction |
| Checked |

| Prediction |
| Checked |

| Prediction |
| Checked |

ice

• **Check your predictions.**

Now try this!

Which materials are the best and worst | conductors | of heat?

metal   plastic   wood

Teachers' note After the children have made their predictions, ask them to explain their reasons. Introduce the term *conductor* for materials that heat up or cool down quickly. Ask the children to predict which spoon will cool the fastest when moved from the pot of hot water to the pot of ice.

Developing Science
Year 4
© A & C BLACK

Hot and cold quiz

Recognise a range of uses of thermal insulators and conductors

- **Write the answers in the speech bubbles. They are all about** conductors **and** insulators .

1. Why is wood a good material for saucepan handles?

1.

2. Why is metal a good material for a saucepan?

2.

3. Why is fish packed in polystyrene for transport?

3.

4. Why do we wrap water pipes in foam rubber?

4.

5. Why are radiators made of metal?

5.

Now try this!

- **Write three other questions and answers about conductors and insulators.**
- **Try them out on a friend.**

Teachers' note Ideally, the children should first have completed pages 35–38. Begin by asking the children about everyday situations when people want to keep things cool or hot or need a material that conducts heat easily, or one that does not. Examples are lagging for pipes, hot water cylinders and lofts, and clothes for keeping people warm.

Developing Science
Year 4
© A & C BLACK

All sorts of solids

Identify and describe solids and observe differences between them

- **Observe the materials. Notice any similarities and differences between them.**

- **Group the materials that are similar to one another. Make notes about this.**

You need

a magnifying glass

flour	sand
gravel	stone
modelling clay	sugar
Plasticine	talcum powder
rubber	wood
salt	

 Do not taste any materials, even if they are foods. It is safe to smell them.

Use as many groups as you need.

1
Notes: _____
_____
_____
_____

3
Notes: _____
_____
_____
_____

Notes: _____
_____
_____
_____
_____

 Now try this!

- **Add another material to each group.**
- **Explain why it belongs to that group.**

Teachers' note Begin by asking the children to identify solid materials in the classroom. Ask them how they can tell if something is solid. Hold up some hollow items (such as an empty box, a hollow chocolate egg and a hollow plastic cube) and ask the children if they are solid. Show them a piece of plastic, break off a piece of chocolate and cut off a piece of the box and ask them if the materials are solid. Point out that solid materials are used for making hollow objects.

Developing Science
Year 4
© **A & C BLACK**

Solid or liquid?

Identify solids and liquids

• **List the solids and liquids in this picture.**

Solids	Liquids

 **Now try this!**

How are solids alike?

How are liquids alike?

What differences do you notice between solids and liquids?

Teachers' note After the children have identified the solids and liquids in the picture, ask them how they knew. Invite them to share their answers, and discuss some of the difficult materials such as honey, jam and yogurt.

**Developing Science
Year 4
© A & C BLACK**

Volume check

Estimate, measure and record volumes

Which container will hold the most water?

- **Predict and record the order:**

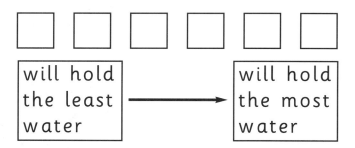

will hold the least water	→	will hold the most water

You need

6 containers that will hold water

A   B   C   D   E   F

a measuring jug

- **Measure the volume of the containers.**
- **Record them on the chart.**
- **List the containers in order:**

holds the least water	→	holds the most water

Container	Volume
A	m l
B	m l
C	m l
D	m l
E	m l
F	m l

- **Check your prediction. Was it right?**

- **Explain any wrong predictions that you or others made.**

What makes it difficult to judge volume by looking at containers?

Teachers' note Revise how to measure the volume of a liquid; ask the children to name the units used. Provide a collection of containers of similar (but not exactly the same) capacities but different shapes. Encourage careful and accurate measurement of volume and discuss what to do if the water from the container will not fit in the measuring jug. Discuss any wrong predictions – especially where the children thought tall containers held more than short ones.

Developing Science
Year 4
© A & C BLACK

Bits and pieces

Understand that solids consisting of very small pieces may behave like liquids

Some solids are made up of small pieces that you can see.

They behave like liquids in many ways.

What can you do with these solids and liquids? ✓ or ✗

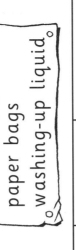

You need
bowl	sieve
cloth	sponge
salt	sugar
sand	water
measuring jug	
paper bags	
washing-up liquid	

sand   salt   sugar   water   washing-up liquid

Material	Pour it into a bowl	Measure its volume in a jug	Pour it through a sieve	Hold it in your hand	Carry it in a paper bag	Mop it up with a cloth	Soak it up with a sponge
Solids							
Liquids							

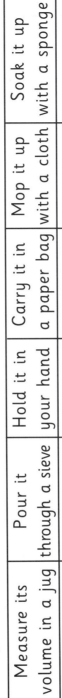

Now try this!

• **Write a definition of** liquid .

Think about the differences between solids and liquids.

Teachers' note The children should first have completed pages 40 and 41. Provide opportunities for them to explore the behaviour of solids consisting of small pieces: sand, dried peas, rice. Ask them in what ways they behave like water and in what ways they are different. Establish that the smaller the pieces the more the solid appears to behave like a liquid. Ask the children if a collection of big pieces of rock can be poured like sand. Ensure that they realise that the difference is only one of scale.

Changes

Understand that the same material can exist as both solid and liquid

Which solids can you change into liquids, and how?

Solid	Can you make it liquid?	How can you change it?
butter		
chocolate		
paper		
sand		
steel		
wax		

Which liquids can you change into solids, and how?

Liquid	Can you make it solid?	How can you change it?
cooking oil		
lemonade		
orange juice		
washing-up liquid		
water		

Now try this!

- **Write three facts about changes from solid to liquid and back.**

   Example: Some materials change from solid to liquid when they are heated.

Teachers' note It would be helpful if the children have completed pages 40, 41 and 43. Ask them if they have seen any solids that have melted and what made this happen. Draw on their previous learning about temperature. How warm does ice have to be to melt? Ask them if all solids will melt. Ask them if they have seen any liquids that have frozen and what made this happen. How cold does water have to be to freeze? Ask them if all liquids will freeze.

Developing Science
Year 4
© A & C BLACK

Meltdown

Understand that different solids melt at different temperatures

Solids that melt always do so at the same temperature.

This temperature is their │melting point│.

- **Link the solids to the thermometer to show their melting points.**

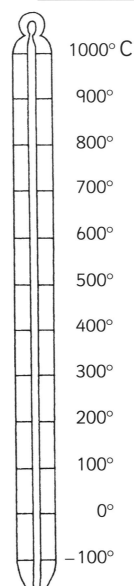

| gold |
| lead |
| polyethylene * |

*sometimes called polythene

| beeswax |
| chocolate |
| butter |
| margarine |
| ice |
| ice cream |

1000° C
900°
800°
700°
600°
500°
400°
300°
200°
100°
0°
−100°

⚠ Ask your teacher which ones you can test.

📖 Use information books, CD-ROMs and the Internet.

Now try this!

- **Draw another thermometer (−50 °C to 50 °C) on which to mark the │freezing points│ of liquids.**

Teachers' note The children should first have completed page 44. Before the children complete the activity sheet ask them to estimate the temperature at which the materials will melt and then to check. Show the children videos or CD-ROMs of materials being heated until they melt and ask them to use other sources to find out about those that were not shown (see page 10).

Developing Science Year 4 © A & C BLACK

45

Sieve it

Understand that mixed solids can be separated

- **Predict which mixtures can be separated using a sieve.**
  ☑ or ☒
- **Find out.**

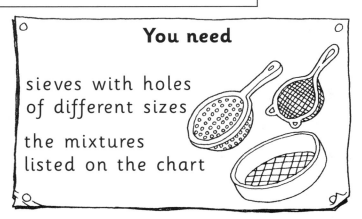

You need

sieves with holes of different sizes

the mixtures listed on the chart

Mixture	Can it be separated using a sieve?		Explanation
	Prediction	**Result**	
dried peas and sand			
salt and sugar			
paper clips, sand and sugar			
dried peas, rice and salt			
flour, salt and sugar			

Now try this!

What could you do to separate the mixtures on which a sieve did not work?

Teachers' note Begin by asking the children to separate a mixture of paper clips and sand. How did they do it? Can they separate sand and rice by hand? Challenge them to think of an easier way. Introduce the idea of using a sieve and ask them to select one with holes of the right size. How did they decide? Draw out the need for the holes to let one material through but not the other.

Developing Science
Year 4
© A & C BLACK

The mad mixer

The mad mixer cannot remember his mixtures because he never makes notes.

You need

a plastic pot
a spoon
water

baking power
beads
chalk
coffee
flour
plaster of Paris
salt
sand
sugar

- **Mix each material with water.**
- **Record your results by drawing lines from the materials to the results.**

baking powder

beads

chalk

coffee

Became solid	Changed colour	Dissolved	Fizzed	Stayed separate

flour

plaster of Paris

salt

sand

sugar

Now try this!

- **Which mixtures can you separate?**
- **Write about what you could do.**

Teachers' note The children should first have completed page 46. Encourage them to make careful observations of what happens when they mix each material with water. What changes to the water do they notice? What changes to the materials do they notice? Ask them to stir each mixture to try to dissolve it. Which materials do they think cannot be separated from water, and why?

**Developing Science
Year 4
© A & C BLACK**

Sieve and filter

Recognise that undissolved solids can be separated from water by filtering

- **Predict: which materials can be separated from water using a sieve and a filter ?**

| baking powder | beads | chalk | flour | rice |
| ground coffee | salt | sand | sugar | |

- **Write them in the outlines.**

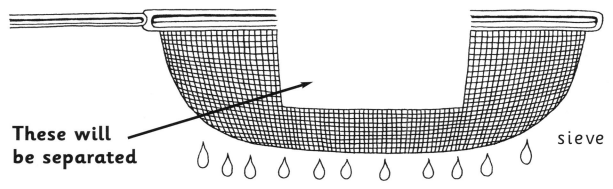

These will be separated

sieve

These will pass through to the filter:

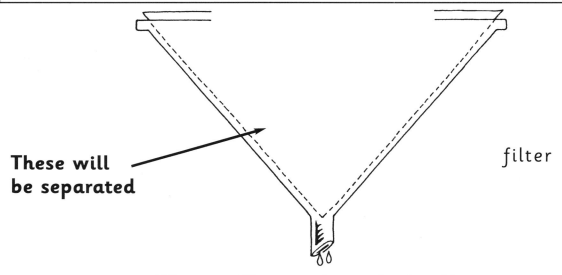

These will be separated

filter

These will pass through the filter:

- **Explain how a sieve and a filter separate materials.**

Teachers' note The children should first have completed pages 46 and 47. Ask them which materials could not be separated from water by sieving. Show them some materials that can be used as filters and ask them if they think these will separate the materials. Draw on their knowledge of filters: coffee filters, teabags and so on.

Developing Science
Year 4
© A & C BLACK

Solutions

When you mix coffee, salt or sugar with water, how can you tell if it is still there?

⚠ Keep everything clean so that it is safe to taste.

- **Make solutions of instant coffee, salt and sugar.**
- **Record your observations:**

You need

beakers   spoons
filter   water
salt   sugar
instant coffee

Material dissolved	How I knew it was still there
coffee	
salt	
sugar	

Draw and write about the tests you can do.

How can you find out if a filter **will separate them from the water?**

_____

_____

_____

_____

_____

_____

Now try this!

- **Explain why some materials cannot be separated by a filter.**

Teachers' note The children should first have completed pages 46–48. Review what they have learned about salt and sugar solutions (that salt and sugar dissolve in water and cannot be separated from it by sieving or filtering). Ask them what happens to the salt and sugar when they are mixed with water. How can they tell if water has sugar or salt in it? Point out that for this activity everything must be kept clean so that tasting is safe.

Developing Science
Year 4
© A & C BLACK

Forcemeters

- **Mark the** forcemeters **to show the forces used for lifting or pulling things.**

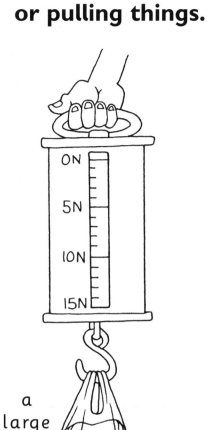

ON
5N
10N
15N

a large stone

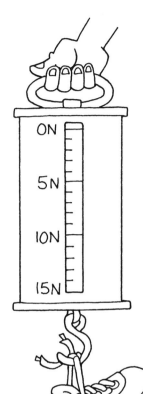

ON
5N
10N
15N

a shoe

ON
5N
10N
15N
20N
25N

a brick

a brick

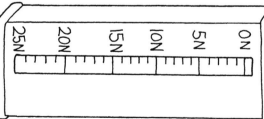
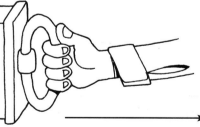

25N 20N 15N 10N 5N ON

Which will need the greatest force?

pulling open a door   moving a chair

- **Predict, then find out.**
- **Record the forces.**

Now try this!

Teachers' note Give the children forcemeters with different scales (see page 11) and investigate what happens when they pull the hook. Ask them what they think they are used for and how they work. Show them how to read the scale, tell them that the newton is the unit of measurement and discuss why forcemeters have different scales. Ask the children to measure the forces needed to lift and pull the objects depicted and to draw the marker on the pictures.

Developing Science
Year 4
© **A & C BLACK**

Surface test

Understand that there is a force between an object and a surface

- **Predict: on which surface will a brick slide most easily?** ✔

carpet ☐   concrete ☐   vinyl tiles ☐   rubber mat ☐

- **Plan an investigation to find out.**

My question:

What I shall do:

I need:

I shall change only this:

I shall keep these the same:

What I shall observe and measure:

How I shall record my findings:

How I shall know the answer to my question:

Teachers' note Ideally, the children should first have completed page 50. Ask them on which surface they think a brick will slide most easily, and why. Discuss how they can use a forcemeter to help them to find out. The results can be recorded on a bar chart.

Developing Science
Year 4
© A & C BLACK

Safe shoes

Understand that the force between two moving surfaces is called *friction*

This was Jason and Gita's question:

This is what they did:

> Which shoes have the best grip on a slippery surface?

> Vinyl floor coverings are slippery.

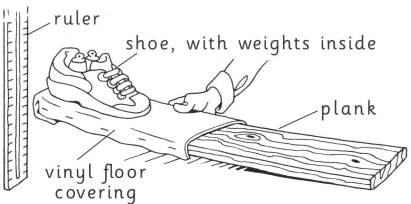

ruler

shoe, with weights inside

plank

vinyl floor covering

They put weights in the shoes to make the test realistic. They lifted the plank and recorded the height at which the shoe started to slide.

They made the test fair. How? _____

_____

_____

Results	
Shoe	**Height at which it slid**
ballet shoe	10 cm
Jason's trainer	98 cm
Mrs Ray's high-heeled shoe	40 cm
Gita's school shoe	80 cm

Which shoe has the best grip?

_____

Which shoe has the worst grip?

_____

For what purposes do shoes need to grip well?

_____

_____

For what purposes should shoes not grip a surface?

_____

Teachers' note The children should first have completed page 51. Ask them if it is a good thing for there to be friction between the soles of shoes and a floor surface, and why. How can they tell how strong the force of friction is between their own shoes and a floor surface in everyday situations?

Developing Science Year 4 © A & C BLACK

Friction

Friction **is a force between two surfaces that acts against movement.**

- **Measure the friction between pairs of surfaces:**

brick wrapped in material

string

forcemeter

pull

floor surface

You need

a brick
a forcemeter
string
a polythene bag
woollen cloth
nylon cloth
a small piece of
    rubber sheeting
a piece of carpet
a rubber mat
vinyl floor
polished wooden
    floor or board

- **Record your results in** newtons **on the chart.**

Floor surface	Material wrapped around brick			
	polythene	wool	nylon	rubber
carpet				
rubber				
vinyl				
polished wood				

- **Complete these sentences:**

The greatest friction was between _____ and _____.

The smallest friction was between _____ and _____.

- **List six places where friction is useful.**
- **List six places where friction is not wanted.**

Teachers' note The children should first have completed pages 50–52. Ask the children if there is always a greater force of friction between an object moving on a rough surface than on a smooth surface, or if the surface of the object makes a difference. Tell them that they are going to measure the force needed to pull materials on different surfaces and to compare pairs of surfaces.

Developing Science
Year 4
© A & C BLACK

Dive bombers

Understand that water resistance slows an object moving through water

Does the shape of an object affect how quickly it sinks in water?

Plasticine

water

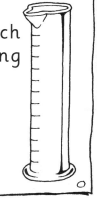

You need

a tall, clear container, such as a measuring cylinder

water

Plasticine

a stopwatch

- **Time how long the Plasticine takes to reach the bottom.**

- **Make the Plasticine into different shapes.**

- **Time how long they take to reach the bottom.**

Make it fair:
use the same piece of Plasticine each time;
use the same amount of water;
drop the Plasticine from the same place.

Shape	Time
⬤ ↓	
⬭ ↓	
⬯ ↓	
▽ ↓	
⬚ ↓	

Does the shape make a difference to the sinking time? ☐

What do you notice about quick-sinking shapes?

_____

_____

_____

_____

_____

- **Make a 'champion dive bomber' and test it against others.**

Teachers' note Talk about the children's experiences of moving though water. What does it feel like when they walk through deep water? Draw out the idea of a force acting against their movement, making it more difficult to move through water than through air.

Developing Science Year 4
© A & C BLACK

Speed boats

Identify trends in results

You need

3 boats like the ones in the pictures

a long plant tray

a battery-powered fan

a stopwatch or timer

paper — thin dowel — wood

Which boat will be the fastest?

A ☐   B ☐   C ☑

- **Find out:**
  - Time each boat.
  - Repeat the test twice.
- Record your results.

Boats		Time (seconds)	0	10	20	30	40	50	60	70	80
A	1st try										
	2nd try										
	3rd try										
B	1st try										
	2nd try										
	3rd try										
C	1st try										
	2nd try										
	3rd try										

Now try this!

Which boat was the fastest? Why?

What does this tell you about the designs of modern racing boats?

Teachers' note Ideally, the children should first have completed page 54. Review their understanding of water resistance and the effect of shape. Discuss why it is important to check their results: factors such as the user's skill with the fan can make a difference. They should look at all three results for each boat to decide which moves the fastest. If the children find it difficult to time the boats, you could race them (you would need a separate tray for each boat).

Developing Science
Year 4
© A & C BLACK

Free fall

- **Drop a ball of Plasticine and a piece of paper.**
- **Describe how they fall:**

Plasticine _____

_____

_____

Paper _____

_____

_____

You need

4 balls of Plasticine – all the same size

4 pieces of paper – all the same size

- **Make a different shape from each ball of Plasticine:**

Use all the Plasticine from each ball.

Work in a group.

- **Drop them all at the same time.**
- **Draw them in order:**

| slowest falling | | | fastest falling |

slowest falling ⟶ fastest falling

- **Repeat this for the paper:**

Screw it into a ball.   Fold it in half.   Fold it into 4.   Leave it as it is.

slowest falling ⟶ fastest falling

Now try this!

- **Change the shape of a piece of paper to make it travel as far as possible when you throw it.**

Teachers' note Provide opportunities for the children to experience air resistance: for example, two children could run across the playground holding a large piece of card vertically between them and feel the force of the air against it. They could also run holding umbrellas behind them and feel the force of the air against them.

Developing Science Year 4 © A & C BLACK

Time for a challenge

- **Drop a cork and watch it fall to the ground.**
- **Make something that will slow the cork's fall as much as possible.**

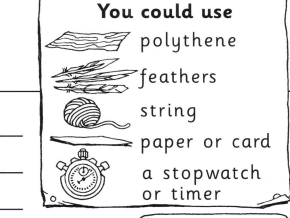

You need

a medium-sized cork

You could use

polythene

feathers

string

paper or card

a stopwatch or timer

Make a labelled drawing. Write about your idea.

This is what I shall make:

This is how we shall know which design works best:

Results	
Design	Time

Teachers' note The children should first have completed page 56. Discuss what would slow the fall of a cork and how its surface area can be increased: for example, the children could add feathers to it so that it resembles a shuttlecock or they could make a parachute for it. Ask them if bigger feathers or a bigger parachute will help. Discuss safe ways of dropping the corks from a height (see page 12).

Developing Science
Year 4
© A & C BLACK

57

Circuit check

Recognise that a complete circuit is needed for a device to work

- **On the chart, explain why these bulbs will not light.**

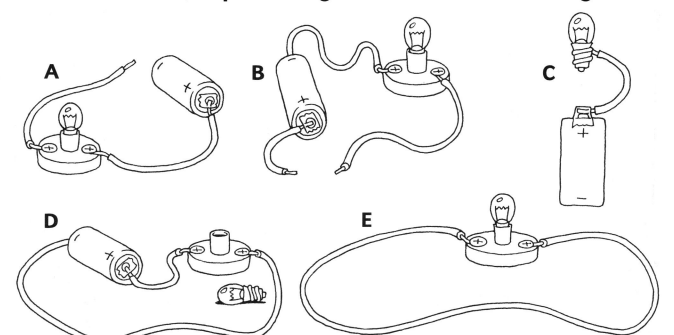

A

B

C

D

E

Circuit	The bulb will not light because ...
A	
B	
C	
D	
E	

Now try this!

- **Re-draw circuits A and C so that the bulbs will light.**
- **Check them by making the circuits. Do the bulbs light?**

Teachers' note Use this activity to introduce the topic of electricity in order to assess the children's understanding of circuits. After they have explained why the bulbs will not light, they could demonstrate their ideas for making them work. Encourage them to use the correct terms for each part of the circuit. They could label these on one of the diagrams.

Developing Science
Year 4
© **A & C BLACK**

Electrical conductors

Understand that some materials conduct electricity better than others

- **Find out which materials** conduct **electricity.**

You need

A circuit with a gap:

bulb — bulb-holder — batteries

battery-holder

crocodile clips

Materials to test:

aluminium	plastic
charcoal	rubber
lead	steel
leather	wood
paper	

- **Clip different materials in the gap.**

- **Record what happens.**

material

crocodile clips

Material	Does the bulb light?	Conductor or insulator?
aluminium		
charcoal		
lead		
leather		
paper		
plastic		
rubber		
steel		
wood		

Now try this!

- **List five objects you think will be conductors.**
- **List five objects you think will be insulators.**
- **Explain your answers.**

Teachers' note The children should first have completed page 58. Show the children a circuit with a gap, as depicted, and ask them what they can do to make the bulb light (they can join the two crocodile clips). Ask them if they can make it work by putting something in the gap. Which materials do they think will work, and why? Introduce the term *conductor* for materials that allow electricity to pass and *insulator* for those that do not.

Developing Science
Year 4
© **A & C BLACK**

Circuit fun

In which of these circuits will the bulb light?

- **Record your answers on the chart.**

A

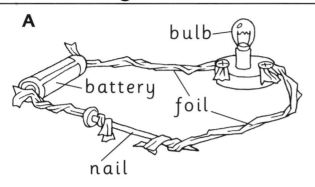

B

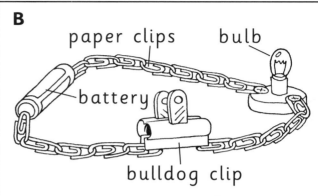

C

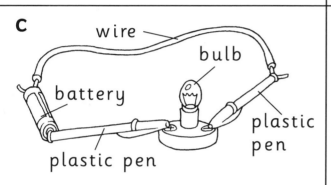

D

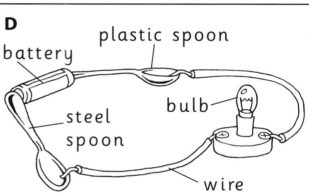

Circuit	Will it work?	Why? or Why not?
A		
B		
C		
D		

- **Find other ways of linking a bulb to a battery without using wire.**

Teachers' note The children should first have completed pages 58–59. Ask them to think about what they have learned about conductors and insulators to help them to decide which circuits will work, and why. Afterwards they could make the circuits – and try making circuits in which they are not allowed to use wire. What other everyday objects can be used to link the bulb and the battery?

Developing Science
Year 4
© **A & C BLACK**

On and off

Understand that a switch can be used to make or break a circuit

• **Make a switch for a circuit.**

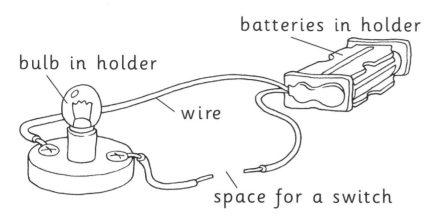

bulb in holder

batteries in holder

wire

space for a switch

You could use

a small piece of soft wood

drawing pins

paper clips

foil

card

• **Draw the circuit with a switch.**

• **Explain how to switch the bulb on and off, and how the switch works.**

Now try this!

• **Examine a manufactured switch.**

• **Draw a diagram to explain how it works.**

Teachers' note The children should first have completed pages 58–59. Show them familiar electrical devices and ask them to identify the switches and to say why these devices have switches. Tell them that they are going to use a battery-powered circuit to investigate switches. Emphasise that it is safe to experiment with batteries but not with mains electricity.

Developing Science
Year 4
© A & C BLACK

Extra power

How can you make these bulbs brighter?

- **Draw and label the changed circuits.**

The bulbs must not burn out!

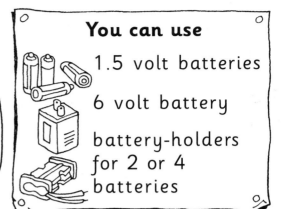

You can use

1.5 volt batteries

6 volt battery

battery-holders for 2 or 4 batteries

4.5V bulb   1.5V battery

2.5V bulb   1.5V battery

6V bulb   1.5V batteries

battery-holder

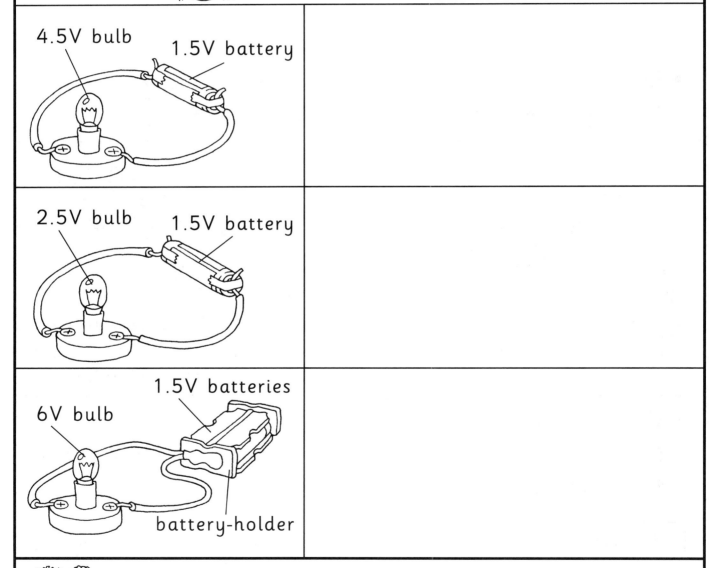

Now try this!

How can you measure the brightness of a bulb?

Teachers' note Show the children a circuit in which a 6V bulb is powered by a 1.5V battery and the bulb is very dim; ask them what they could do to make it brighter. Try out their ideas and ask them if the bulb could be made brighter and brighter by adding more and more batteries. Tell them that if too much power is given to a bulb it will burn out.

Developing Science
Year 4
© **A & C BLACK**

Extra bulbs

What will happen when you add bulbs to a circuit?

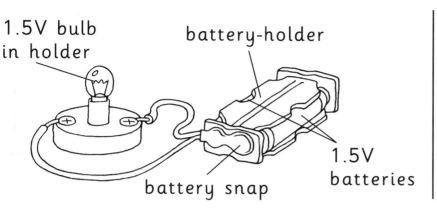

1.5V bulb in holder

battery-holder

battery snap

1.5V batteries

paper

- **Look at the bulb through some sheets of paper.**

  Through how many sheets can you see it? ☐

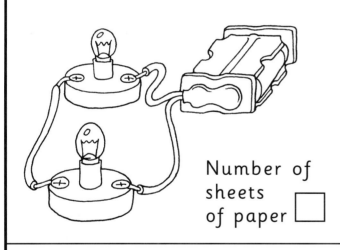

Number of sheets of paper ☐

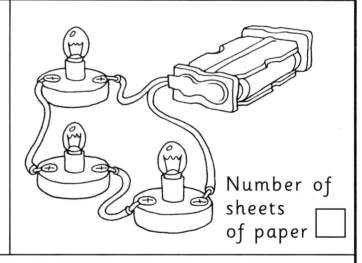

Number of sheets of paper ☐

- **Continue to add 1.5 V bulbs.**

- **Record the number of sheets of paper through which the bulbs can be seen.**

Number of bulbs	1	2	3	4	5	6
Number of sheets of paper they shine through						

Teachers' note The children should first have completed page 62. Ask them what will happen if a bulb is added to a circuit. Will both bulbs light? Will they be as bright as one bulb? Discuss how to measure the brightness. Ask the children to make the circuit in the first picture, measure the brightness of the bulb, and then add bulbs, measuring the brightness each time. The paper 'brightness meter' should be held at the same distance from each bulb to make the test fair.

Developing Science Year 4
© A & C BLACK

Speed it up

Shaina has made a fan using a motor:

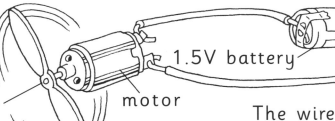

1.5V battery

wire

propeller

motor

The wires are fixed onto the battery with sticky tape.

The fan is very slow.

How can Shaina speed it up?

Keep your fingers away from propellers.

• **Draw your idea and try it out.**

How well did your idea work?

_____

_____

Now try this!

• **Find a way of measuring the speed of the fan.**

• **Measure the speed each time you add a battery to the circuit.**

Teachers' note The children should first have completed page 62. Make the circuit shown in the picture and let the children try it out. They should hold the motor at the end where the wires are attached. Ask them to stop the motor working (they could add a switch to the circuit) and to say why they think it turned very slowly.

Developing Science Year 4
© A & C BLACK